Proverbs 31:15

2023
CHRISTIAN WEEKLY PLANNER

THIS PLANNER BELONGS TO:

_____

_____

_____

JANUARY

M	T	W	T	F	S	S
						1
2	3	4	5	6	7	8
9	10	11	12	13	14	15
16	17	18	19	20	21	22
23	24	25	26	27	28	29
30	31					

FEBRUARY

M	T	W	T	F	S	S
		1	2	3	4	5
6	7	8	9	10	11	12
13	14	15	16	17	18	19
20	21	22	23	24	25	26
27	28					

MARCH

M	T	W	T	F	S	S
		1	2	3	4	5
6	7	8	9	10	11	12
13	14	15	16	17	18	19
20	21	22	23	24	25	26
27	28	29	30	31		

APRIL

M	T	W	T	F	S	S
					1	2
3	4	5	6	7	8	9
10	11	12	13	14	15	16
17	18	19	20	21	22	23
24	25	26	27	28	29	30

MAY

M	T	W	T	F	S	S
1	2	3	4	5	6	7
8	9	10	11	12	13	14
15	16	17	18	19	20	21
22	23	24	25	26	27	28
29	30	31				

JUNE

M	T	W	T	F	S	S
			1	2	3	4
5	6	7	8	9	10	11
12	13	14	15	16	17	18
19	20	21	22	23	24	25
26	27	28	29	30		

JULY

M	T	W	T	F	S	S
					1	2
3	4	5	6	7	8	9
10	11	12	13	14	15	16
17	18	19	20	21	22	23
24	25	26	27	28	29	30
31						

AUGUST

M	T	W	T	F	S	S
	1	2	3	4	5	6
7	8	9	10	11	12	13
14	15	16	17	18	19	20
21	22	23	24	25	26	27
28	29	30	31			

SEPTEMBER

M	T	W	T	F	S	S
				1	2	3
4	5	6	7	8	9	10
11	12	13	14	15	16	17
18	19	20	21	22	23	24
25	26	27	28	29	30	

OCTOBER

M	T	W	T	F	S	S
						1
2	3	4	5	6	7	8
9	10	11	12	13	14	15
16	17	18	19	20	21	22
23	24	25	26	27	28	29
30	31					

NOVEMBER

M	T	W	T	F	S	S
		1	2	3	4	5
6	7	8	9	10	11	12
13	14	15	16	17	18	19
20	21	22	23	24	25	26
27	28	29	30			

DECEMBER

M	T	W	T	F	S	S
				1	2	3
4	5	6	7	8	9	10
11	12	13	14	15	16	17
18	19	20	21	22	23	24
25	26	27	28	29	30	31

JANUARY

TOP 3 GOALS	MONDAY	TUESDAY	WEDNESDAY
#1			
#2			
#3			
TO DO'S			
○	2	3	4
○			
○			
○			
○	9	10	11
○			
○			
GRATEFUL FOR ...			
	16	17	18
	23	24	25
REMINDER			
	30	31	

THURSDAY	FRIDAY	SATURDAY	SUNDAY
			1
5	6	7	8
12	13	14	15
19	20	21	22
26	27	28	29

NOTES

MONTHLY EXPENSES

JANUARY

DATE	DESCRIPTION	AMOUNT	BALANCE
		TOTAL EXPENSE:	

HABIT TRACKER

JANUARY

HABIT							
1	○	○	○	○	○	○	○
2	○	○	○	○	○	○	○
3	○	○	○	○	○	○	○
4	○	○	○	○	○	○	○
5	○	○	○	○	○	○	○
6	○	○	○	○	○	○	○
7	○	○	○	○	○	○	○
8	○	○	○	○	○	○	○
9	○	○	○	○	○	○	○
10	○	○	○	○	○	○	○
11	○	○	○	○	○	○	○
12	○	○	○	○	○	○	○
13	○	○	○	○	○	○	○
14	○	○	○	○	○	○	○
15	○	○	○	○	○	○	○
16	○	○	○	○	○	○	○
17	○	○	○	○	○	○	○
18	○	○	○	○	○	○	○
19	○	○	○	○	○	○	○
20	○	○	○	○	○	○	○
21	○	○	○	○	○	○	○
22	○	○	○	○	○	○	○
23	○	○	○	○	○	○	○
24	○	○	○	○	○	○	○
25	○	○	○	○	○	○	○
26	○	○	○	○	○	○	○
27	○	○	○	○	○	○	○
28	○	○	○	○	○	○	○
29	○	○	○	○	○	○	○
30	○	○	○	○	○	○	○
31	○	○	○	○	○	○	○

WEEK 52

Prayers answered last week

Goals

#1

#2

#3

Groceries

MONDAY 26

◯

◯

◯

Bible reading:

TUESDAY 27

◯

◯

◯

Bible reading:

WEDNESDAY 28

◯

◯

◯

Bible reading:

DECEMBER | JANUARY

Prayers for this week

I am grateful for ...

_____

_____

How/who I will bless ...

_____

_____

THURSDAY 29

_____

_____

_____

◯

◯

◯

Bible reading:

FRIDAY 30

_____

_____

_____

◯

◯

◯

Bible reading:

SATURDAY 31

_____

_____

Bible reading:

SUNDAY 1

_____

_____

Bible reading:

WEEK 1

Prayers answered last week

Goals

#1

#2

#3

Groceries

MONDAY 2

◯

◯

◯

Bible reading:

TUESDAY 3

◯

◯

◯

Bible reading:

WEDNESDAY 4

◯

◯

◯

Bible reading:

Prayers for this week

I am grateful for ...

How/who I will bless ...

THURSDAY 5

◯

◯

◯

Bible reading:

FRIDAY 6

◯

◯

◯

Bible reading:

SATURDAY 7

Bible reading:

SUNDAY 8

Bible reading:

WEEK 2

Prayers answered last week

Goals

#1

#2

#3

Groceries

MONDAY 9

◯

◯

◯

Bible reading:

TUESDAY 10

◯

◯

◯

Bible reading:

WEDNESDAY 11

◯

◯

◯

Bible reading:

JANUARY

Prayers for this week

I am grateful for ...

How/who I will bless ...

THURSDAY 12

◯
◯
◯

Bible reading:

FRIDAY 13

◯
◯
◯

Bible reading:

SATURDAY 14

Bible reading:

SUNDAY 15

Bible reading:

WEEK 3

Prayers answered last week

Goals

#1

#2

#3

Groceries

MONDAY 16

◯

◯

◯

Bible reading:

TUESDAY 17

◯

◯

◯

Bible reading:

WEDNESDAY 18

◯

◯

◯

Bible reading:

JANUARY

Prayers for this week

I am grateful for ...

How/who I will bless ...

THURSDAY 19

◯

◯

◯

Bible reading:

FRIDAY 20

◯

◯

◯

Bible reading:

SATURDAY 21

Bible reading:

SUNDAY 22

Bible reading:

WEEK 4

Prayers answered last week

Goals

#1

#2

#3

Groceries

MONDAY 23

◯

◯

◯

Bible reading:

TUESDAY 24

◯

◯

◯

Bible reading:

WEDNESDAY 25

◯

◯

◯

Bible reading:

Prayers for this week

I am grateful for ...

_____

_____

_____

How/who I will bless ...

_____

_____

_____

THURSDAY 26

_____

_____

_____

◯

◯

◯

Bible reading:

FRIDAY 27

_____

_____

_____

◯

◯

◯

Bible reading:

SATURDAY 28

_____

_____

_____

Bible reading:

SUNDAY 29

_____

_____

_____

Bible reading:

FEBRUARY

TOP 3 GOALS	MONDAY	TUESDAY	WEDNESDAY
#1			1
#2			
#3			
TO DO'S			
◯	6	7	8
◯			
◯			
◯			
◯	13	14	15
◯			
◯			
GRATEFUL FOR ...			
	20	21	22
	27	28	
REMINDER			

THURSDAY	FRIDAY	SATURDAY	SUNDAY
2	3	4	5
9	10	11	12
16	17	18	19
23	24	25	26

NOTES

MONTHLY EXPENSES

FEBRUARY

DATE	DESCRIPTION	AMOUNT	BALANCE
		TOTAL EXPENSE:	

HABIT TRACKER
FEBRUARY

HABIT							
1	○	○	○	○	○	○	○
2	○	○	○	○	○	○	○
3	○	○	○	○	○	○	○
4	○	○	○	○	○	○	○
5	○	○	○	○	○	○	○
6	○	○	○	○	○	○	○
7	○	○	○	○	○	○	○
8	○	○	○	○	○	○	○
9	○	○	○	○	○	○	○
10	○	○	○	○	○	○	○
11	○	○	○	○	○	○	○
12	○	○	○	○	○	○	○
13	○	○	○	○	○	○	○
14	○	○	○	○	○	○	○
15	○	○	○	○	○	○	○
16	○	○	○	○	○	○	○
17	○	○	○	○	○	○	○
18	○	○	○	○	○	○	○
19	○	○	○	○	○	○	○
20	○	○	○	○	○	○	○
21	○	○	○	○	○	○	○
22	○	○	○	○	○	○	○
23	○	○	○	○	○	○	○
24	○	○	○	○	○	○	○
25	○	○	○	○	○	○	○
26	○	○	○	○	○	○	○
27	○	○	○	○	○	○	○
28	○	○	○	○	○	○	○

WEEK 5

Prayers answered last week

Goals

#1

#2

#3

Groceries

MONDAY 30

◯

◯

◯

Bible reading:

TUESDAY 31

◯

◯

◯

Bible reading:

WEDNESDAY 1

◯

◯

◯

Bible reading:

Prayers for this week

I am grateful for ...

_____

_____

_____

How/who I will bless ...

_____

_____

_____

THURSDAY 2

_____

_____

_____

_____

◯

◯

◯

Bible reading:

FRIDAY 3

_____

_____

_____

_____

◯

◯

◯

Bible reading:

SATURDAY 4

_____

_____

_____

Bible reading:

SUNDAY 5

_____

_____

_____

Bible reading:

WEEK 6

Prayers answered last week

Goals

#1

#2

#3

Groceries

MONDAY 6

○

○

○

Bible reading:

TUESDAY 7

○

○

○

Bible reading:

WEDNESDAY 8

○

○

○

Bible reading:

Prayers for this week

I am grateful for ...

_____

_____

_____

How/who I will bless ...

_____

_____

_____

THURSDAY 9

_____

_____

_____

◯

◯

◯

Bible reading:

FRIDAY 10

_____

_____

_____

◯

◯

◯

Bible reading:

SATURDAY 11

_____

_____

_____

Bible reading:

SUNDAY 12

_____

_____

_____

Bible reading:

WEEK 7

Prayers answered last week

Goals

#1

#2

#3

Groceries

MONDAY 13

○

○

○

Bible reading:

TUESDAY 14

○

○

○

Bible reading:

WEDNESDAY 15

○

○

○

Bible reading:

Prayers for this week

I am grateful for ...

_____

_____

_____

How/who I will bless ...

_____

_____

_____

THURSDAY 16

_____

_____

_____

○

○

○

Bible reading: _____

FRIDAY 17

_____

_____

_____

○

○

○

Bible reading: _____

SATURDAY 18

_____

_____

_____

Bible reading: _____

SUNDAY 19

_____

_____

_____

Bible reading: _____

WEEK 8

Prayers answered last week

Goals

#1

#2

#3

Groceries

MONDAY 20

◯

◯

◯

Bible reading:

TUESDAY 21

◯

◯

◯

Bible reading:

WEDNESDAY 22

◯

◯

◯

Bible reading:

Prayers for this week

I am grateful for ...

_____

_____

How/who I will bless ...

_____

_____

THURSDAY 23

_____

_____

_____

_____

○

○

○

Bible reading:

FRIDAY 24

_____

_____

_____

_____

○

○

○

Bible reading:

SATURDAY 25

_____

_____

_____

Bible reading:

SUNDAY 26

_____

_____

_____

Bible reading:

MARCH

TOP 3 GOALS	MONDAY	TUESDAY	WEDNESDAY
#1			1
#2			
#3			
TO DO'S			
◯	6	7	8
◯			
◯			
◯			
◯	13	14	15
◯			
◯			
GRATEFUL FOR ...			
	20	21	22
	27	28	29
REMINDER			

THURSDAY	FRIDAY	SATURDAY	SUNDAY
2	3	4	5
9	10	11	12
16	17	18	19
23	24	25	26
30	31		

NOTES

MONTHLY EXPENSES

MARCH

DATE	DESCRIPTION	AMOUNT	BALANCE
	TOTAL EXPENSE:		

HABIT TRACKER

MARCH

HABIT							
1	○	○	○	○	○	○	○
2	○	○	○	○	○	○	○
3	○	○	○	○	○	○	○
4	○	○	○	○	○	○	○
5	○	○	○	○	○	○	○
6	○	○	○	○	○	○	○
7	○	○	○	○	○	○	○
8	○	○	○	○	○	○	○
9	○	○	○	○	○	○	○
10	○	○	○	○	○	○	○
11	○	○	○	○	○	○	○
12	○	○	○	○	○	○	○
13	○	○	○	○	○	○	○
14	○	○	○	○	○	○	○
15	○	○	○	○	○	○	○
16	○	○	○	○	○	○	○
17	○	○	○	○	○	○	○
18	○	○	○	○	○	○	○
19	○	○	○	○	○	○	○
20	○	○	○	○	○	○	○
21	○	○	○	○	○	○	○
22	○	○	○	○	○	○	○
23	○	○	○	○	○	○	○
24	○	○	○	○	○	○	○
25	○	○	○	○	○	○	○
26	○	○	○	○	○	○	○
27	○	○	○	○	○	○	○
28	○	○	○	○	○	○	○
29	○	○	○	○	○	○	○
30	○	○	○	○	○	○	○
31	○	○	○	○	○	○	○

WEEK 9

Prayers answered last week

Goals

#1

#2

#3

Groceries

MONDAY 27

◯

◯

◯

Bible reading:

TUESDAY 28

◯

◯

◯

Bible reading:

WEDNESDAY 1

◯

◯

◯

Bible reading:

Prayers for this week

I am grateful for ...

_____

_____

_____

How/who I will bless ...

_____

_____

THURSDAY 2

_____

_____

_____

_____

◯

◯

◯

Bible reading:

FRIDAY 3

_____

_____

_____

_____

◯

◯

◯

Bible reading:

SATURDAY 4

_____

_____

_____

Bible reading:

SUNDAY 5

_____

_____

_____

Bible reading:

WEEK 10

Prayers answered last week

Goals

#1

#2

#3

Groceries

MONDAY 6

○

○

○

Bible reading:

TUESDAY 7

○

○

○

Bible reading:

WEDNESDAY 8

○

○

○

Bible reading:

Prayers for this week

I am grateful for ...

_____

_____

_____

How/who I will bless ...

_____

_____

_____

THURSDAY 9

_____

_____

_____

◯

◯

◯

Bible reading:

FRIDAY 10

_____

_____

_____

◯

◯

◯

Bible reading:

SATURDAY 11

_____

_____

Bible reading:

SUNDAY 12

_____

_____

Bible reading:

WEEK 11

Prayers answered last week

Goals

#1

#2

#3

Groceries

MONDAY 13

◯

◯

◯

Bible reading:

TUESDAY 14

◯

◯

◯

Bible reading:

WEDNESDAY 15

◯

◯

◯

Bible reading:

Prayers for this week

I am grateful for ...

_____

_____

_____

How/who I will bless ...

_____

_____

_____

THURSDAY 16

_____

_____

_____

_____

◯

◯

◯

Bible reading:

FRIDAY 17

_____

_____

_____

_____

◯

◯

◯

Bible reading:

SATURDAY 18

_____

_____

Bible reading:

SUNDAY 19

_____

_____

Bible reading:

WEEK 12

Prayers answered last week

Goals

#1

#2

#3

Groceries

MONDAY 20

◯

◯

◯

Bible reading:

TUESDAY 21

◯

◯

◯

Bible reading:

WEDNESDAY 22

◯

◯

◯

Bible reading:

Prayers for this week

I am grateful for ...

How/who I will bless ...

THURSDAY 23

◯

◯

◯

Bible reading:

FRIDAY 24

◯

◯

◯

Bible reading:

SATURDAY 25

Bible reading:

SUNDAY 26

Bible reading:

WEEK 13

Prayers answered last week

Goals

#1

#2

#3

Groceries

MONDAY 27

◯

◯

◯

Bible reading:

TUESDAY 28

◯

◯

◯

Bible reading:

WEDNESDAY 29

◯

◯

◯

Bible reading:

Prayers for this week

I am grateful for ...

_____

_____

_____

How/who I will bless ...

_____

_____

_____

THURSDAY 30

....

....

....

○

○

○

Bible reading:

FRIDAY 31

....

....

....

○

○

○

Bible reading:

SATURDAY 1

_____

....

_____

Bible reading:

SUNDAY 2

_____

....

_____

Bible reading:

APRIL

TOP 3 GOALS	MONDAY	TUESDAY	WEDNESDAY
#1			
#2			
#3			
TO DO'S			
○	3	4	5
○			
○			
○			
○	10	11	12
○			
○			
GRATEFUL FOR ...			
	17	18	19
	24	25	26
REMINDER			

THURSDAY	FRIDAY	SATURDAY	SUNDAY
		1	2
6	7	8	9
13	14	15	16
20	21	22	23
27	28	29	30

NOTES

MONTHLY EXPENSES

APRIL

DATE	DESCRIPTION	AMOUNT	BALANCE
	TOTAL EXPENSE:		

HABIT TRACKER

HABIT							
1	○	○	○	○	○	○	○
2	○	○	○	○	○	○	○
3	○	○	○	○	○	○	○
4	○	○	○	○	○	○	○
5	○	○	○	○	○	○	○
6	○	○	○	○	○	○	○
7	○	○	○	○	○	○	○
8	○	○	○	○	○	○	○
9	○	○	○	○	○	○	○
10	○	○	○	○	○	○	○
11	○	○	○	○	○	○	○
12	○	○	○	○	○	○	○
13	○	○	○	○	○	○	○
14	○	○	○	○	○	○	○
15	○	○	○	○	○	○	○
16	○	○	○	○	○	○	○
17	○	○	○	○	○	○	○
18	○	○	○	○	○	○	○
19	○	○	○	○	○	○	○
20	○	○	○	○	○	○	○
21	○	○	○	○	○	○	○
22	○	○	○	○	○	○	○
23	○	○	○	○	○	○	○
24	○	○	○	○	○	○	○
25	○	○	○	○	○	○	○
26	○	○	○	○	○	○	○
27	○	○	○	○	○	○	○
28	○	○	○	○	○	○	○
29	○	○	○	○	○	○	○
30	○	○	○	○	○	○	○

WEEK 14

Prayers answered last week

Goals

#1

#2

#3

Groceries

MONDAY 3

○

○

○

Bible reading:

TUESDAY 4

○

○

○

Bible reading:

WEDNESDAY 5

○

○

○

Bible reading:

Prayers for this week

I am grateful for ...

_____

_____

_____

How/who I will bless ...

_____

_____

_____

THURSDAY 6

_____

_____

_____

○

○

○

Bible reading:

FRIDAY 7

_____

_____

_____

○

○

○

Bible reading:

SATURDAY 8

_____

_____

_____

Bible reading:

SUNDAY 9

_____

_____

_____

Bible reading:

WEEK 15

Prayers answered last week

Goals

#1

#2

#3

Groceries

MONDAY 10

○

○

○

Bible reading:

TUESDAY 11

○

○

○

Bible reading:

WEDNESDAY 12

○

○

○

Bible reading:

Prayers for this week

I am grateful for ...

_____
_____
_____

How/who I will bless ...

_____
_____
_____

THURSDAY 13

_____
_____
_____
_____

◯
◯
◯

Bible reading:

FRIDAY 14

_____
_____
_____
_____

◯
◯
◯

Bible reading:

SATURDAY 15

_____
_____
_____

Bible reading:

SUNDAY 16

_____
_____
_____

Bible reading:

WEEK 16

Prayers answered last week

Goals

#1

#2

#3

Groceries

MONDAY 17

◯

◯

◯

Bible reading:

TUESDAY 18

◯

◯

◯

Bible reading:

WEDNESDAY 19

◯

◯

◯

Bible reading:

Prayers for this week

I am grateful for ...

How/who I will bless ...

THURSDAY 20

◯

◯

◯

Bible reading:

FRIDAY 21

◯

◯

◯

Bible reading:

SATURDAY 22

Bible reading:

SUNDAY 23

Bible reading:

WEEK 17

Prayers answered last week

Goals

#1

#2

#3

Groceries

MONDAY 24

◯

◯

◯

Bible reading:

TUESDAY 25

◯

◯

◯

Bible reading:

WEDNESDAY 26

◯

◯

◯

Bible reading:

Prayers for this week

I am grateful for ...

_____

_____

_____

How/who I will bless ...

_____

_____

_____

THURSDAY 27

_____

_____

_____

_____

◯

◯

◯

Bible reading:

FRIDAY 28

_____

_____

_____

_____

◯

◯

◯

Bible reading:

SATURDAY 29

_____

_____

_____

Bible reading:

SUNDAY 30

_____

_____

_____

Bible reading:

MAY

TOP 3 GOALS	MONDAY	TUESDAY	WEDNESDAY
#1	1	2	3
#2			
#3			
TO DO'S			
○	8	9	10
○			
○			
○			
○	15	16	17
○			
○			
GRATEFUL FOR ...			
	22	23	24
	29	30	31
REMINDER			

2023

THURSDAY	FRIDAY	SATURDAY	SUNDAY
4	5	6	7
11	12	13	14
18	19	20	21
25	26	27	28

NOTES

MONTHLY EXPENSES

MAY

DATE	DESCRIPTION	AMOUNT	BALANCE
TOTAL EXPENSE:			

HABIT TRACKER

MAY

HABIT							
1	○	○	○	○	○	○	○
2	○	○	○	○	○	○	○
3	○	○	○	○	○	○	○
4	○	○	○	○	○	○	○
5	○	○	○	○	○	○	○
6	○	○	○	○	○	○	○
7	○	○	○	○	○	○	○
8	○	○	○	○	○	○	○
9	○	○	○	○	○	○	○
10	○	○	○	○	○	○	○
11	○	○	○	○	○	○	○
12	○	○	○	○	○	○	○
13	○	○	○	○	○	○	○
14	○	○	○	○	○	○	○
15	○	○	○	○	○	○	○
16	○	○	○	○	○	○	○
17	○	○	○	○	○	○	○
18	○	○	○	○	○	○	○
19	○	○	○	○	○	○	○
20	○	○	○	○	○	○	○
21	○	○	○	○	○	○	○
22	○	○	○	○	○	○	○
23	○	○	○	○	○	○	○
24	○	○	○	○	○	○	○
25	○	○	○	○	○	○	○
26	○	○	○	○	○	○	○
27	○	○	○	○	○	○	○
28	○	○	○	○	○	○	○
29	○	○	○	○	○	○	○
30	○	○	○	○	○	○	○
31	○	○	○	○	○	○	○

WEEK 18

Prayers answered last week

Goals

#1

#2

#3

Groceries

MONDAY 1

◯

◯

◯

Bible reading:

TUESDAY 2

◯

◯

◯

Bible reading:

WEDNESDAY 3

◯

◯

◯

Bible reading:

Prayers for this week

I am grateful for ...

How/who I will bless ...

THURSDAY 4

○

○

○

Bible reading:

FRIDAY 5

○

○

○

Bible reading:

SATURDAY 6

Bible reading:

SUNDAY 7

Bible reading:

WEEK 19

Prayers answered last week

Goals

#1 _____

#2 _____

#3 _____

Groceries

_____
_____
_____

MONDAY 8

_____
_____
_____
_____

◯
◯
◯

Bible reading:

TUESDAY 9

_____
_____
_____
_____

◯
◯
◯

Bible reading:

WEDNESDAY 10

_____
_____
_____

◯
◯
◯

Bible reading:

Prayers for this week

I am grateful for ...

How/who I will bless ...

THURSDAY 11

Bible reading:

FRIDAY 12

Bible reading:

SATURDAY 13

SUNDAY 14

Bible reading:

Bible reading:

WEEK 20

Prayers answered last week

Goals

#1

#2

#3

Groceries

MONDAY 15

◯

◯

◯

Bible reading:

TUESDAY 16

◯

◯

◯

Bible reading:

WEDNESDAY 17

◯

◯

◯

Bible reading:

Prayers for this week

I am grateful for ...

_____

_____

_____

How/who I will bless ...

_____

_____

_____

THURSDAY 18

_____

_____

_____

_____

◯

◯

◯

Bible reading:

FRIDAY 19

_____

_____

_____

_____

◯

◯

◯

Bible reading:

SATURDAY 20

_____

_____

Bible reading:

SUNDAY 21

_____

_____

Bible reading:

WEEK 21

Prayers answered last week

Goals

#1

#2

#3

Groceries

MONDAY 22

◯

◯

◯

Bible reading:

TUESDAY 23

◯

◯

◯

Bible reading:

WEDNESDAY 24

◯

◯

◯

Bible reading:

Prayers for this week

I am grateful for ...

_____

_____

_____

How/who I will bless ...

_____

_____

_____

THURSDAY 25

_____

_____

_____

_____

○

○

○

Bible reading:

FRIDAY 26

_____

_____

_____

_____

○

○

○

Bible reading:

SATURDAY 27

_____

_____

_____

Bible reading:

SUNDAY 28

_____

_____

_____

Bible reading:

JUNE

TOP 3 GOALS	MONDAY	TUESDAY	WEDNESDAY
#1			
#2			
#3			
TO DO'S			
○	5	6	7
○			
○			
○			
○	12	13	14
○			
○			
GRATEFUL FOR ...			
	19	20	21
	26	27	28
REMINDER			

2023

THURSDAY	FRIDAY	SATURDAY	SUNDAY
1	2	3	4
8	9	10	11
15	16	17	18
22	23	24	25
29	30		

NOTES

MONTHLY EXPENSES

JUNE

DATE	DESCRIPTION	AMOUNT	BALANCE
		TOTAL EXPENSE:	

HABIT							
1	○	○	○	○	○	○	○
2	○	○	○	○	○	○	○
3	○	○	○	○	○	○	○
4	○	○	○	○	○	○	○
5	○	○	○	○	○	○	○
6	○	○	○	○	○	○	○
7	○	○	○	○	○	○	○
8	○	○	○	○	○	○	○
9	○	○	○	○	○	○	○
10	○	○	○	○	○	○	○
11	○	○	○	○	○	○	○
12	○	○	○	○	○	○	○
13	○	○	○	○	○	○	○
14	○	○	○	○	○	○	○
15	○	○	○	○	○	○	○
16	○	○	○	○	○	○	○
17	○	○	○	○	○	○	○
18	○	○	○	○	○	○	○
19	○	○	○	○	○	○	○
20	○	○	○	○	○	○	○
21	○	○	○	○	○	○	○
22	○	○	○	○	○	○	○
23	○	○	○	○	○	○	○
24	○	○	○	○	○	○	○
25	○	○	○	○	○	○	○
26	○	○	○	○	○	○	○
27	○	○	○	○	○	○	○
28	○	○	○	○	○	○	○
29	○	○	○	○	○	○	○
30	○	○	○	○	○	○	○

WEEK 22

Prayers answered last week

Goals

#1

#2

#3

Groceries

MONDAY 29

○

○

○

Bible reading:

TUESDAY 30

○

○

○

Bible reading:

WEDNESDAY 31

○

○

○

Bible reading:

Prayers for this week

I am grateful for ...

_____

_____

_____

How/who I will bless ...

_____

_____

_____

THURSDAY 1

_____

_____

_____

◯
◯
◯

Bible reading:

FRIDAY 2

_____

_____

_____

◯
◯
◯

Bible reading:

SATURDAY 3

_____

_____

_____

Bible reading:

SUNDAY 4

_____

_____

_____

Bible reading:

WEEK 23

Prayers answered last week

Goals

#1

#2

#3

Groceries

MONDAY 5

○

○

○

Bible reading:

TUESDAY 6

○

○

○

Bible reading:

WEDNESDAY 7

○

○

○

Bible reading:

Prayers for this week

I am grateful for ...

How/who I will bless ...

THURSDAY 8

◯
◯
◯

Bible reading:

FRIDAY 9

◯
◯
◯

Bible reading:

SATURDAY 10

Bible reading:

SUNDAY 11

Bible reading:

WEEK 24

Prayers answered last week

Goals

#1

#2

#3

Groceries

MONDAY 12

○

○

○

Bible reading:

TUESDAY 13

○

○

○

Bible reading:

WEDNESDAY 14

○

○

○

Bible reading:

Prayers for this week

I am grateful for ...

_____

_____

_____

How/who I will bless ...

_____

_____

_____

THURSDAY 15

_____

_____

_____

○

○

○

Bible reading:

FRIDAY 16

_____

_____

_____

○

○

○

Bible reading:

SATURDAY 17

_____

_____

_____

Bible reading:

SUNDAY 18

_____

_____

_____

Bible reading:

WEEK 25

Prayers answered last week

Goals

#1

#2

#3

Groceries

MONDAY 19

○

○

○

Bible reading:

TUESDAY 20

○

○

○

Bible reading:

WEDNESDAY 21

○

○

○

Bible reading:

Prayers for this week

I am grateful for ...

_____

_____

_____

How/who I will bless ...

_____

_____

_____

THURSDAY 22

_____

_____

_____

_____

◯

◯

◯

Bible reading:

FRIDAY 23

_____

_____

_____

_____

◯

◯

◯

Bible reading:

SATURDAY 24

_____

_____

_____

Bible reading:

SUNDAY 25

_____

_____

_____

Bible reading:

WEEK 26

Prayers answered last week

Goals

#1

#2

#3

Groceries

MONDAY 26

◯

◯

◯

Bible reading:

TUESDAY 27

◯

◯

◯

Bible reading:

WEDNESDAY 28

◯

◯

◯

Bible reading:

JUNE | JULY

Prayers for this week

I am grateful for ...

_____

_____

How/who I will bless ...

_____

_____

THURSDAY 29

_____

_____

_____

◯

◯

◯

Bible reading:

FRIDAY 30

_____

_____

_____

◯

◯

◯

Bible reading:

SATURDAY 1

_____

_____

_____

Bible reading:

SUNDAY 2

_____

_____

_____

Bible reading:

JULY

TOP 3 GOALS	MONDAY	TUESDAY	WEDNESDAY
#1			
#2			
#3			
TO DO'S			
○	3	4	5
○			
○			
○			
○	10	11	12
○			
○			
GRATEFUL FOR ...			
	17	18	19
	24	25	26
REMINDER			
	31		

THURSDAY	FRIDAY	SATURDAY	SUNDAY
		1	2
6	7	8	9
13	14	15	16
20	21	22	23
27	28	29	30

NOTES

MONTHLY EXPENSES

JULY

DATE	DESCRIPTION	AMOUNT	BALANCE
		TOTAL EXPENSE:	

HABIT TRACKER
JULY

HABIT							
1	○	○	○	○	○	○	○
2	○	○	○	○	○	○	○
3	○	○	○	○	○	○	○
4	○	○	○	○	○	○	○
5	○	○	○	○	○	○	○
6	○	○	○	○	○	○	○
7	○	○	○	○	○	○	○
8	○	○	○	○	○	○	○
9	○	○	○	○	○	○	○
10	○	○	○	○	○	○	○
11	○	○	○	○	○	○	○
12	○	○	○	○	○	○	○
13	○	○	○	○	○	○	○
14	○	○	○	○	○	○	○
15	○	○	○	○	○	○	○
16	○	○	○	○	○	○	○
17	○	○	○	○	○	○	○
18	○	○	○	○	○	○	○
19	○	○	○	○	○	○	○
20	○	○	○	○	○	○	○
21	○	○	○	○	○	○	○
22	○	○	○	○	○	○	○
23	○	○	○	○	○	○	○
24	○	○	○	○	○	○	○
25	○	○	○	○	○	○	○
26	○	○	○	○	○	○	○
27	○	○	○	○	○	○	○
28	○	○	○	○	○	○	○
29	○	○	○	○	○	○	○
30	○	○	○	○	○	○	○
31	○	○	○	○	○	○	○

WEEK 27

Prayers answered last week

Goals

#1

#2

#3

Groceries

MONDAY 3

○

○

○

Bible reading:

TUESDAY 4

○

○

○

Bible reading:

WEDNESDAY 5

○

○

○

Bible reading:

Prayers for this week

I am grateful for ...

How/who I will bless ...

THURSDAY 6

○
○
○

Bible reading:

FRIDAY 7

○
○
○

Bible reading:

SATURDAY 8

Bible reading:

SUNDAY 9

Bible reading:

WEEK 28

Prayers answered last week

Goals

#1

#2

#3

Groceries

MONDAY 10

◯

◯

◯

Bible reading:

TUESDAY 11

◯

◯

◯

Bible reading:

WEDNESDAY 12

◯

◯

◯

Bible reading:

Prayers for this week

I am grateful for ...

_____

_____

_____

How/who I will bless ...

_____

_____

_____

THURSDAY 13

_____

_____

_____

_____

◯

◯

◯

Bible reading:

FRIDAY 14

_____

_____

_____

_____

◯

◯

◯

Bible reading:

SATURDAY 15

_____

_____

_____

Bible reading:

SUNDAY 16

_____

_____

_____

Bible reading:

WEEK 29

Prayers answered last week

Goals

#1

#2

#3

Groceries

MONDAY 17

○

○

○

Bible reading:

TUESDAY 18

○

○

○

Bible reading:

WEDNESDAY 19

○

○

○

Bible reading:

Prayers for this week

I am grateful for ...

_____

_____

_____

How/who I will bless ...

_____

_____

_____

THURSDAY 20

_____

_____

_____

_____

○

○

○

Bible reading:

FRIDAY 21

_____

_____

_____

_____

○

○

○

Bible reading:

SATURDAY 22

_____

_____

_____

Bible reading:

SUNDAY 23

_____

_____

_____

Bible reading:

WEEK 30

Prayers answered last week

Goals

#1

#2

#3

Groceries

MONDAY 24

◯

◯

◯

Bible reading:

TUESDAY 25

◯

◯

◯

Bible reading:

WEDNESDAY 26

◯

◯

◯

Bible reading:

Prayers for this week

I am grateful for ...

_____

_____

_____

How/who I will bless ...

_____

_____

_____

THURSDAY 27

_____

_____

_____

_____

○ _____

○ _____

○ _____

Bible reading:

FRIDAY 28

_____

_____

_____

_____

○ _____

○ _____

○ _____

Bible reading:

SATURDAY 29

_____

_____

_____

Bible reading:

SUNDAY 30

_____

_____

_____

Bible reading:

AUGUST

TOP 3 GOALS	MONDAY	TUESDAY	WEDNESDAY
#1		1	2
#2			
#3			
TO DO'S			
◯	7	8	9
◯			
◯			
◯			
◯	14	15	16
◯			
◯			
GRATEFUL FOR ...			
	21	22	23
	28	29	30
REMINDER			

THURSDAY	FRIDAY	SATURDAY	SUNDAY
3	4	5	6
10	11	12	13
17	18	19	20
24	25	26	27
31			

NOTES

MONTHLY EXPENSES

AUGUST

DATE	DESCRIPTION	AMOUNT	BALANCE
	TOTAL EXPENSE:		

HABIT TRACKER

AUGUST

HABIT							
1	◯	◯	◯	◯	◯	◯	◯
2	◯	◯	◯	◯	◯	◯	◯
3	◯	◯	◯	◯	◯	◯	◯
4	◯	◯	◯	◯	◯	◯	◯
5	◯	◯	◯	◯	◯	◯	◯
6	◯	◯	◯	◯	◯	◯	◯
7	◯	◯	◯	◯	◯	◯	◯
8	◯	◯	◯	◯	◯	◯	◯
9	◯	◯	◯	◯	◯	◯	◯
10	◯	◯	◯	◯	◯	◯	◯
11	◯	◯	◯	◯	◯	◯	◯
12	◯	◯	◯	◯	◯	◯	◯
13	◯	◯	◯	◯	◯	◯	◯
14	◯	◯	◯	◯	◯	◯	◯
15	◯	◯	◯	◯	◯	◯	◯
16	◯	◯	◯	◯	◯	◯	◯
17	◯	◯	◯	◯	◯	◯	◯
18	◯	◯	◯	◯	◯	◯	◯
19	◯	◯	◯	◯	◯	◯	◯
20	◯	◯	◯	◯	◯	◯	◯
21	◯	◯	◯	◯	◯	◯	◯
22	◯	◯	◯	◯	◯	◯	◯
23	◯	◯	◯	◯	◯	◯	◯
24	◯	◯	◯	◯	◯	◯	◯
25	◯	◯	◯	◯	◯	◯	◯
26	◯	◯	◯	◯	◯	◯	◯
27	◯	◯	◯	◯	◯	◯	◯
28	◯	◯	◯	◯	◯	◯	◯
29	◯	◯	◯	◯	◯	◯	◯
30	◯	◯	◯	◯	◯	◯	◯
31	◯	◯	◯	◯	◯	◯	◯

WEEK 31

Prayers answered last week

Goals

#1

#2

#3

Groceries

MONDAY 31

○

○

○

Bible reading:

TUESDAY 1

○

○

○

Bible reading:

WEDNESDAY 2

○

○

○

Bible reading:

Prayers for this week

I am grateful for ...

_____

_____

_____

How/who I will bless ...

_____

_____

_____

THURSDAY 3

_____

_____

_____

○ _____

○ _____

○ _____

Bible reading: _____

FRIDAY 4

_____

_____

_____

○ _____

○ _____

○ _____

Bible reading: _____

SATURDAY 5

_____

_____

_____

Bible reading: _____

SUNDAY 6

_____

_____

_____

Bible reading: _____

WEEK 32

Prayers answered last week

Goals

#1

#2

#3

Groceries

MONDAY 7

○

○

○

Bible reading:

TUESDAY 8

○

○

○

Bible reading:

WEDNESDAY 9

○

○

○

Bible reading:

AUGUST

Prayers for this week

I am grateful for ...

How/who I will bless ...

THURSDAY 10

○
○
○

Bible reading:

FRIDAY 11

○
○
○

Bible reading:

SATURDAY 12

Bible reading:

SUNDAY 13

Bible reading:

WEEK 33

Prayers answered last week

Goals

#1

#2

#3

Groceries

MONDAY 14

◯

◯

◯

Bible reading:

TUESDAY 15

◯

◯

◯

Bible reading:

WEDNESDAY 16

◯

◯

◯

Bible reading:

Prayers for this week

I am grateful for ...

_____

_____

_____

How/who I will bless ...

_____

_____

_____

THURSDAY 17

_____

_____

_____

_____

◯ _____

◯ _____

◯ _____

Bible reading: _____

FRIDAY 18

_____

_____

_____

_____

◯ _____

◯ _____

◯ _____

Bible reading: _____

SATURDAY 19

_____

_____

_____

Bible reading: _____

SUNDAY 20

_____

_____

_____

Bible reading: _____

WEEK 34

Prayers answered last week

Goals

#1

#2

#3

Groceries

MONDAY 21

◯

◯

◯

Bible reading:

TUESDAY 22

◯

◯

◯

Bible reading:

WEDNESDAY 23

◯

◯

◯

Bible reading:

AUGUST

Prayers for this week

I am grateful for ...

_____

_____

_____

How/who I will bless ...

_____

_____

_____

THURSDAY 24

_____

_____

_____

_____

◯

◯

◯

Bible reading:

FRIDAY 25

_____

_____

_____

_____

◯

◯

◯

Bible reading:

SATURDAY 26

_____

_____

_____

Bible reading:

SUNDAY 27

_____

_____

_____

Bible reading:

WEEK 35

Prayers answered last week

Goals

#1 _____

#2 _____

#3 _____

Groceries

_____

_____

_____

MONDAY 28

_____

_____

_____

○

○

○

Bible reading: _____

TUESDAY 29

_____

_____

_____

○

○

○

Bible reading: _____

WEDNESDAY 30

_____

_____

_____

○

○

○

Bible reading: _____

Prayers for this week

I am grateful for …

_____

_____

How/who I will bless …

_____

_____

THURSDAY 31

_____

_____

_____

_____

◯

◯

◯

Bible reading:

FRIDAY 1

_____

_____

_____

_____

◯

◯

◯

Bible reading:

SATURDAY 2

_____

_____

_____

Bible reading:

SUNDAY 3

_____

_____

_____

Bible reading:

SEPTEMBER

TOP 3 GOALS	MONDAY	TUESDAY	WEDNESDAY
#1			
#2			
#3			
TO DO'S			
○	4	5	6
○			
○			
○			
○	11	12	13
○			
○			
GRATEFUL FOR ...			
	18	19	20
	25	26	27
REMINDER			

THURSDAY	FRIDAY	SATURDAY	SUNDAY
	1	2	3
7	8	9	10
14	15	16	17
21	22	23	24
28	29	30	

NOTES

MONTHLY EXPENSES

SEPTEMBER

DATE	DESCRIPTION	AMOUNT	BALANCE
	TOTAL EXPENSE:		

HABIT TRACKER
SEPTEMBER

HABIT							
1	○	○	○	○	○	○	○
2	○	○	○	○	○	○	○
3	○	○	○	○	○	○	○
4	○	○	○	○	○	○	○
5	○	○	○	○	○	○	○
6	○	○	○	○	○	○	○
7	○	○	○	○	○	○	○
8	○	○	○	○	○	○	○
9	○	○	○	○	○	○	○
10	○	○	○	○	○	○	○
11	○	○	○	○	○	○	○
12	○	○	○	○	○	○	○
13	○	○	○	○	○	○	○
14	○	○	○	○	○	○	○
15	○	○	○	○	○	○	○
16	○	○	○	○	○	○	○
17	○	○	○	○	○	○	○
18	○	○	○	○	○	○	○
19	○	○	○	○	○	○	○
20	○	○	○	○	○	○	○
21	○	○	○	○	○	○	○
22	○	○	○	○	○	○	○
23	○	○	○	○	○	○	○
24	○	○	○	○	○	○	○
25	○	○	○	○	○	○	○
26	○	○	○	○	○	○	○
27	○	○	○	○	○	○	○
28	○	○	○	○	○	○	○
29	○	○	○	○	○	○	○
30	○	○	○	○	○	○	○

WEEK 36

Prayers answered last week

Goals

#1

#2

#3

Groceries

MONDAY 4

○

○

○

Bible reading:

TUESDAY 5

○

○

○

Bible reading:

WEDNESDAY 6

○

○

○

Bible reading:

Prayers for this week

I am grateful for ...

_____

_____

_____

How/who I will bless ...

_____

_____

_____

THURSDAY 7

_____

_____

_____

_____

○

○

○

Bible reading:

FRIDAY 8

_____

_____

_____

_____

○

○

○

Bible reading:

SATURDAY 9

_____

_____

_____

Bible reading:

SUNDAY 10

_____

_____

_____

Bible reading:

WEEK 37

Prayers answered last week

Goals

#1

#2

#3

Groceries

MONDAY 11

◯

◯

◯

Bible reading:

TUESDAY 12

◯

◯

◯

Bible reading:

WEDNESDAY 13

◯

◯

◯

Bible reading:

Prayers for this week

I am grateful for ...

_____
_____
_____
_____

How/who I will bless ...

_____
_____
_____
_____

THURSDAY 14

_____
_____
_____
_____

◯
◯
◯

Bible reading: _____

FRIDAY 15

_____
_____
_____
_____

◯
◯
◯

Bible reading: _____

SATURDAY 16

_____
_____
_____

Bible reading: _____

SUNDAY 17

_____
_____
_____

Bible reading: _____

WEEK 38

Goals

#1 _____

#2 _____

#3 _____

Groceries

_____

_____

_____

MONDAY 18

_____

_____

_____

_____

◯

◯

◯

Bible reading: _____

TUESDAY 19

_____

_____

_____

_____

◯

◯

◯

Bible reading: _____

WEDNESDAY 20

_____

_____

_____

_____

◯

◯

◯

Bible reading: _____

Prayers for this week

I am grateful for ...

_____

_____

_____

How/who I will bless ...

_____

_____

_____

THURSDAY 21

_____

_____

_____

_____

◯

◯

◯

Bible reading:
_____

FRIDAY 22

_____

_____

_____

◯

◯

◯

Bible reading:
_____

SATURDAY 23

_____

_____

_____

Bible reading:
_____

SUNDAY 24

_____

_____

_____

Bible reading:
_____

WEEK 39

Prayers answered last week

Goals

#1

#2

#3

Groceries

MONDAY 25

◯

◯

◯

Bible reading:

TUESDAY 26

◯

◯

◯

Bible reading:

WEDNESDAY 27

◯

◯

◯

Bible reading:

Prayers for this week

I am grateful for ...

_____
_____
_____
_____

How/who I will bless ...

_____
_____
_____

THURSDAY 28

_____
_____
_____

○
○
○

Bible reading:

FRIDAY 29

_____
_____
_____

○
○
○

Bible reading:

SATURDAY 30

_____
_____
_____

Bible reading:

SUNDAY 1

_____
_____
_____

Bible reading:

OCTOBER

TOP 3 GOALS	MONDAY	TUESDAY	WEDNESDAY
#1			
#2			
#3			
TO DO'S			
◯	2	3	4
◯			
◯			
◯			
◯	9	10	11
◯			
◯			
GRATEFUL FOR ...			
	16	17	18
	23	24	25
REMINDER			
	30	31	

2023

THURSDAY	FRIDAY	SATURDAY	SUNDAY
			1
5	6	7	8
12	13	14	15
19	20	21	22
26	27	28	29

NOTES

MONTHLY EXPENSES

OCTOBER

DATE	DESCRIPTION	AMOUNT	BALANCE
		TOTAL EXPENSE:	

HABIT TRACKER

OCTOBER

HABIT							
1	○	○	○	○	○	○	○
2	○	○	○	○	○	○	○
3	○	○	○	○	○	○	○
4	○	○	○	○	○	○	○
5	○	○	○	○	○	○	○
6	○	○	○	○	○	○	○
7	○	○	○	○	○	○	○
8	○	○	○	○	○	○	○
9	○	○	○	○	○	○	○
10	○	○	○	○	○	○	○
11	○	○	○	○	○	○	○
12	○	○	○	○	○	○	○
13	○	○	○	○	○	○	○
14	○	○	○	○	○	○	○
15	○	○	○	○	○	○	○
16	○	○	○	○	○	○	○
17	○	○	○	○	○	○	○
18	○	○	○	○	○	○	○
19	○	○	○	○	○	○	○
20	○	○	○	○	○	○	○
21	○	○	○	○	○	○	○
22	○	○	○	○	○	○	○
23	○	○	○	○	○	○	○
24	○	○	○	○	○	○	○
25	○	○	○	○	○	○	○
26	○	○	○	○	○	○	○
27	○	○	○	○	○	○	○
28	○	○	○	○	○	○	○
29	○	○	○	○	○	○	○
30	○	○	○	○	○	○	○
31	○	○	○	○	○	○	○

WEEK 40

Prayers answered last week

Goals

#1 _____

#2 _____

#3 _____

Groceries

_____

_____

_____

MONDAY 2

_____

_____

_____

_____

◯ _____

◯ _____

◯ _____

Bible reading: _____

TUESDAY 3

_____

_____

_____

_____

◯ _____

◯ _____

◯ _____

Bible reading: _____

WEDNESDAY 4

_____

_____

_____

_____

◯ _____

◯ _____

◯ _____

Bible reading: _____

OCTOBER

Prayers for this week

I am grateful for ...

_____

_____

_____

How/who I will bless ...

_____

_____

_____

THURSDAY 5

_____

_____

_____

○
○
○

Bible reading:

FRIDAY 6

_____

_____

_____

○
○
○

Bible reading:

SATURDAY 7

_____

_____

_____

Bible reading:

SUNDAY 8

_____

_____

_____

Bible reading:

WEEK 41

Prayers answered last week

Goals

#1

#2

#3

Groceries

MONDAY 9

◯

◯

◯

Bible reading:

TUESDAY 10

◯

◯

◯

Bible reading:

WEDNESDAY 11

◯

◯

◯

Bible reading:

OCTOBER

Prayers for this week

I am grateful for ...

How/who I will bless ...

THURSDAY 12

◯
◯
◯

Bible reading:

FRIDAY 13

◯
◯
◯

Bible reading:

SATURDAY 14

Bible reading:

SUNDAY 15

Bible reading:

WEEK 42

Prayers answered last week

Goals

#1

#2

#3

Groceries

MONDAY 16

◯

◯

◯

Bible reading:

TUESDAY 17

◯

◯

◯

Bible reading:

WEDNESDAY 18

◯

◯

◯

Bible reading:

OCTOBER

Prayers for this week

I am grateful for ...

_____

_____

_____

How/who I will bless ...

_____

_____

_____

THURSDAY 19

_____

_____

_____

_____

○

○

○

Bible reading:

FRIDAY 20

_____

_____

_____

_____

○

○

○

Bible reading:

SATURDAY 21

_____

_____

_____

Bible reading:

SUNDAY 22

_____

_____

_____

Bible reading:

WEEK 43

Prayers answered last week

Goals

#1 _____

#2 _____

#3 _____

Groceries

_____

_____

_____

MONDAY 23

_____

_____

_____

_____

○

○

○

Bible reading: _____

TUESDAY 24

_____

_____

_____

_____

○

○

○

Bible reading: _____

WEDNESDAY 25

_____

_____

_____

_____

○

○

○

Bible reading: _____

Prayers for this week

I am grateful for ...

How/who I will bless ...

THURSDAY 26

◯
◯
◯

Bible reading:

FRIDAY 27

◯
◯
◯

Bible reading:

SATURDAY 28

Bible reading:

SUNDAY 29

Bible reading:

NOVEMBER

TOP 3 GOALS	MONDAY	TUESDAY	WEDNESDAY
#1			1
#2			
#3			
TO DO'S			
○	6	7	8
○			
○			
○			
○	13	14	15
○			
○			
GRATEFUL FOR ...			
	20	21	22
	27	28	29
REMINDER			

THURSDAY	FRIDAY	SATURDAY	SUNDAY
2	3	4	5
9	10	11	12
16	17	18	19
23	24	25	26
30			

NOTES

MONTHLY EXPENSES

NOVEMBER

DATE	DESCRIPTION	AMOUNT	BALANCE
		TOTAL EXPENSE:	

HABIT TRACKER

NOVEMBER

HABIT							
1	○	○	○	○	○	○	○
2	○	○	○	○	○	○	○
3	○	○	○	○	○	○	○
4	○	○	○	○	○	○	○
5	○	○	○	○	○	○	○
6	○	○	○	○	○	○	○
7	○	○	○	○	○	○	○
8	○	○	○	○	○	○	○
9	○	○	○	○	○	○	○
10	○	○	○	○	○	○	○
11	○	○	○	○	○	○	○
12	○	○	○	○	○	○	○
13	○	○	○	○	○	○	○
14	○	○	○	○	○	○	○
15	○	○	○	○	○	○	○
16	○	○	○	○	○	○	○
17	○	○	○	○	○	○	○
18	○	○	○	○	○	○	○
19	○	○	○	○	○	○	○
20	○	○	○	○	○	○	○
21	○	○	○	○	○	○	○
22	○	○	○	○	○	○	○
23	○	○	○	○	○	○	○
24	○	○	○	○	○	○	○
25	○	○	○	○	○	○	○
26	○	○	○	○	○	○	○
27	○	○	○	○	○	○	○
28	○	○	○	○	○	○	○
29	○	○	○	○	○	○	○
30	○	○	○	○	○	○	○

WEEK 44

Prayers answered last week

Goals

#1

#2

#3

Groceries

MONDAY 30

○

○

○

Bible reading:

TUESDAY 31

○

○

○

Bible reading:

WEDNESDAY 1

○

○

○

Bible reading:

Prayers for this week

I am grateful for ...

_____

_____

_____

How/who I will bless ...

_____

_____

_____

THURSDAY 2

_____

_____

_____

_____

○

○

○

Bible reading:

FRIDAY 3

_____

_____

_____

_____

○

○

○

Bible reading:

SATURDAY 4

_____

_____

_____

Bible reading:

SUNDAY 5

_____

_____

_____

Bible reading:

WEEK 45

Prayers answered last week

Goals

#1

#2

#3

Groceries

MONDAY 6

○

○

○

Bible reading:

TUESDAY 7

○

○

○

Bible reading:

WEDNESDAY 8

○

○

○

Bible reading:

Prayers for this week

I am grateful for ...

_____

_____

_____

How/who I will bless ...

_____

_____

_____

THURSDAY 9

_____

_____

_____

_____

◯ _____

◯ _____

◯ _____

Bible reading: _____

FRIDAY 10

_____

_____

_____

_____

◯ _____

◯ _____

◯ _____

Bible reading: _____

SATURDAY 11

_____

_____

_____

Bible reading: _____

SUNDAY 12

_____

_____

_____

Bible reading: _____

WEEK 46

Prayers answered last week

Goals

#1

#2

#3

Groceries

MONDAY 13

◯

◯

◯

Bible reading:

TUESDAY 14

◯

◯

◯

Bible reading:

WEDNESDAY 15

◯

◯

◯

Bible reading:

Prayers for this week

I am grateful for ...

How/who I will bless ...

THURSDAY 16

◯

◯

◯

Bible reading:

FRIDAY 17

◯

◯

◯

Bible reading:

SATURDAY 18

Bible reading:

SUNDAY 19

Bible reading:

WEEK 47

Prayers answered last week

Goals

#1

#2

#3

Groceries

MONDAY 20

◯

◯

◯

Bible reading:

TUESDAY 21

◯

◯

◯

Bible reading:

WEDNESDAY 22

◯

◯

◯

Bible reading:

NOVEMBER

Prayers for this week

I am grateful for ...

_____

_____

_____

How/who I will bless ...

_____

_____

_____

THURSDAY 23

_____

_____

_____

○

○

○

Bible reading:

FRIDAY 24

_____

_____

_____

○

○

○

Bible reading:

SATURDAY 25

_____

_____

_____

Bible reading:

SUNDAY 26

_____

_____

_____

Bible reading:

WEEK 48

Prayers answered last week

Goals

#1

#2

#3

Groceries

MONDAY 27

○

○

○

Bible reading:

TUESDAY 28

○

○

○

Bible reading:

WEDNESDAY 29

○

○

○

Bible reading:

Prayers for this week

I am grateful for ...

_____

_____

_____

How/who I will bless ...

_____

_____

_____

THURSDAY 30

_____

_____

_____

◯ _____

◯ _____

◯ _____

Bible reading:

FRIDAY 1

_____

_____

_____

◯ _____

◯ _____

◯ _____

Bible reading:

SATURDAY 2

_____

_____

_____

Bible reading:

SUNDAY 3

_____

_____

_____

Bible reading:

DECEMBER

TOP 3 GOALS	MONDAY	TUESDAY	WEDNESDAY
#1			
#2			
#3			
TO DO'S			
○	4	5	6
○			
○			
○			
○	11	12	13
○			
○			
GRATEFUL FOR ...			
	18	19	20
	25	26	27
REMINDER			

2023

THURSDAY	FRIDAY	SATURDAY	SUNDAY
	1	2	3
7	8	9	10
14	15	16	17
21	22	23	24
28	29	30	31

NOTES

MONTHLY EXPENSES

DECEMBER

DATE	DESCRIPTION	AMOUNT	BALANCE
	TOTAL EXPENSE:		

HABIT TRACKER
DECEMBER

HABIT							
1	○	○	○	○	○	○	○
2	○	○	○	○	○	○	○
3	○	○	○	○	○	○	○
4	○	○	○	○	○	○	○
5	○	○	○	○	○	○	○
6	○	○	○	○	○	○	○
7	○	○	○	○	○	○	○
8	○	○	○	○	○	○	○
9	○	○	○	○	○	○	○
10	○	○	○	○	○	○	○
11	○	○	○	○	○	○	○
12	○	○	○	○	○	○	○
13	○	○	○	○	○	○	○
14	○	○	○	○	○	○	○
15	○	○	○	○	○	○	○
16	○	○	○	○	○	○	○
17	○	○	○	○	○	○	○
18	○	○	○	○	○	○	○
19	○	○	○	○	○	○	○
20	○	○	○	○	○	○	○
21	○	○	○	○	○	○	○
22	○	○	○	○	○	○	○
23	○	○	○	○	○	○	○
24	○	○	○	○	○	○	○
25	○	○	○	○	○	○	○
26	○	○	○	○	○	○	○
27	○	○	○	○	○	○	○
28	○	○	○	○	○	○	○
29	○	○	○	○	○	○	○
30	○	○	○	○	○	○	○
31	○	○	○	○	○	○	○

WEEK 49

Prayers answered last week

Goals

#1

#2

#3

Groceries

MONDAY 4

○

○

○

Bible reading:

TUESDAY 5

○

○

○

Bible reading:

WEDNESDAY 6

○

○

○

Bible reading:

DECEMBER

Prayers for this week

I am grateful for ...

_____

_____

_____

How/who I will bless ...

_____

_____

_____

THURSDAY 7

_____

_____

_____

◯

◯

◯

Bible reading:

FRIDAY 8

_____

_____

_____

◯

◯

◯

Bible reading:

SATURDAY 9

_____

_____

Bible reading:

SUNDAY 10

_____

_____

Bible reading:

WEEK 50

Prayers answered last week

Goals

#1

#2

#3

Groceries

MONDAY 11

○

○

○

Bible reading:

TUESDAY 12

○

○

○

Bible reading:

WEDNESDAY 13

○

○

○

Bible reading:

Prayers for this week

I am grateful for ...

_____

_____

_____

How/who I will bless ...

_____

_____

_____

THURSDAY 14

_____

_____

_____

_____

◯ _____

◯ _____

◯ _____

Bible reading: _____

FRIDAY 15

_____

_____

_____

_____

◯ _____

◯ _____

◯ _____

Bible reading: _____

SATURDAY 16

_____

_____

Bible reading: _____

SUNDAY 17

_____

_____

Bible reading: _____

WEEK 51

Prayers answered last week

Goals

#1 _____

#2 _____

#3 _____

Groceries

_____

_____

MONDAY 18

_____

_____

_____

○

○

○

Bible reading: _____

TUESDAY 19

_____

_____

_____

○

○

○

Bible reading: _____

WEDNESDAY 20

_____

_____

_____

○

○

○

Bible reading: _____

Prayers for this week

I am grateful for ...

_____

_____

_____

How/who I will bless ...

_____

_____

_____

THURSDAY 21

....

....

....

....

◯

◯

◯

Bible reading:

FRIDAY 22

....

....

....

....

◯

◯

◯

Bible reading:

SATURDAY 23

_____

_____

_____

Bible reading:

SUNDAY 24

_____

_____

_____

Bible reading:

WEEK 52

Goals

#1

#2

#3

Groceries

MONDAY 25

○

○

○

Bible reading:

TUESDAY 26

○

○

○

Bible reading:

WEDNESDAY 27

○

○

○

Bible reading:

Prayers for this week

I am grateful for ...

_____

_____

_____

How/who I will bless ...

_____

_____

_____

THURSDAY 28

_____

_____

_____

○

○

○

Bible reading:

FRIDAY 29

_____

_____

_____

○

○

○

Bible reading:

SATURDAY 30

_____

_____

Bible reading:

SUNDAY 31

_____

_____

Bible reading:

CONTACTS

NAME	PHONE	EMAIL

CONTACTS

NAME	PHONE	EMAIL

CONTACTS

NAME	PHONE	EMAIL

CONTACTS

NAME	PHONE	EMAIL

NOTES

NOTES

NOTES

NOTES

NOTES

NOTES